BETTER
Together

100 PROMPTS
FOR
A HAPPIER,
HEALTHIER
RELATIONSHIP

Why this Journal?

Intentionally filling space in your relationship with creativity and connection can help provide the rhythm and excitement you're seeking. We created 100 prompts for 100 days to foster a happier, healthier relationship by helping you develop greater perspective, deeper admiration, and sincere self-love.

HOW TO USE THIS JOURNAL

We believe that love is both a choice and a skill—and like any skill, love takes work. This journal is intended to help *you* improve your relationship by taking just a few minutes each day to fill out the provided prompts.

Write

Spend at least 3-5 minutes each day writing. Below are a few key principles to help you get the most out of your time:

Put in Effort: You'll get back what you put in on this, so be thoughtful about what you write. For example, if a prompt asks you to write about something you appreciate about your partner, don't simply list "they're nice". Take the time to describe *why* you appreciate their kindness. Describe how their kindness impacted the rest of your day. Write about some of the nice things they have done for you recently. So on and so forth. Put some effort in—it'll make a difference.

Be Honest: Some of these questions might be a little challenging, that's ok, they are intended to be. But rather than writing down the way you *wish* things were or going for easy, but lazy answers, take the time to find the *real* answers. For example: If the prompt asks you "do you rely on your partner for your own happiness?" rather than simply writing "no," be thoughtful and do a little soul-searching. Think about what ways you might be.

Be Kind: Remember why you picked up this journal in the first place—to improve your relationship. The intent of these prompts is to increase positivity and foster admiration, so be kind.

Reflect

Often times, after pouring our hearts out in a journal entry, we close the book and never read what we wrote ever again—essentially a "brain dump." We recommend that immediately after you finish writing, you take a minute to read what you wrote—this brings the exercise full circle and helps keep what you wrote fresh in your mind throughout the day.

FAQs

Should I do this with my partner, or by myself?

Ideally, both you and your partner will each work on these journal prompts, although writing your responses in your own respective journals—but don't fret if your partner is too busy or uninterested in using this journal right now, you will still see great benefits from using this by yourself as well.

How frequently should I use this?

Every day for 100 days. But if you forget, don't beat yourself up, just pick up where you left off. Remember, one of the core aims of this journal is to develop positive, lasting changes in the way that you think about yourself, your partner, and your relationship. To make those changes, you will need to develop new habits that require effort and consistency.

Why questions about self-love?

These questions seem less intuitive, as they don't appear to have anything to do with the relationship. But that is simply not the case. Tony Robbins said: "The only way a relationship will last is if you see your relationship as a place that you go to give, and not a place that you go to take." Self-love is critical because if you don't love yourself, you will try to take from your partner to fill the void in your life, rather than give love to them freely.

How does this help?

Habits run our lives. They affect the way we walk, the way we talk, and yes—the way we think and interact with others. Many of us, at one point in our lives or another, have developed less than ideal habits—which ultimately affect our relationships. We complain, we criticize, and we fail to appreciate. Of course, we don't want to act that way, but change can be difficult.

By now, you've probably heard the term "neuroplasticity"—essentially the brain's ability to change itself. So, for example, if the brain has developed a habit of thinking negatively, we can literally change our brain to think positively—to make thinking positively the new "norm" for our brain. And one of the most effective ways to unlock the superpower of neuroplasticity is by, you guessed it, writing.

" The grass is greener where you water it"

- Neil Barringham

"Do what you did at the beginning of your relationship, and there won't be an end."

- Anthony Robbins

Describe in detail your first date with your partner.

_____

_____

_____

_____

_____

_____

_____

_____

_____

_____

_____

_____

_____

_____

_____

_____

_____

_____

_____

_____

"Three things
in human life are important:
the first is to be kind;
the second is to be kind;
and the third is to be kind."

-Henry James

Write about some of the kindest things that you have seen your partner do for someone other than yourself.

_____

_____

_____

_____

_____

_____

_____

_____

_____

_____

_____

_____

_____

_____

_____

_____

_____

_____

_____

_____

"The grass is greener where you water it."

- Neil Barringham

What do you wish were different in your relationship?
What are you willing to do to make that happen?

_____

_____

_____

_____

_____

_____

_____

_____

_____

_____

_____

_____

_____

_____

_____

_____

_____

_____

_____

"A relationship is like a house. When a lightbulb burns out you do not go and buy a new house, you fix the light bulb"

- Unknown

Describe an experience that refined you as a partnership.

_____

_____

_____

_____

_____

_____

_____

_____

_____

_____

_____

_____

_____

_____

_____

_____

_____

_____

_____

_____

"Love cures people— both the ones who give it and the ones who receive it."

- Karl Menninger

What are some things that your partner feels insecure about? How can you support them through these specific insecurities?

_____

_____

_____

_____

_____

_____

_____

_____

_____

_____

_____

_____

_____

_____

_____

_____

_____

_____

_____

_____

_____

_____

"If you understand each other you will be kind to each other."

- John Steinbeck

Write about your partner's upbringing.
What challenges did they face?

_____

_____

_____

_____

_____

_____

_____

_____

_____

_____

_____

_____

_____

_____

_____

_____

_____

_____

_____

_____

"To be trusted is a greater compliment than being loved."

- George MacDonald

Describe a time when you felt confidence in your partner.

_____

_____

_____

_____

_____

_____

_____

_____

_____

_____

_____

_____

_____

_____

_____

_____

_____

_____

_____

_____

"The more grateful I am, the more beauty I see."
— Mary Davis

What did your partner do today that you appreciated?

_____

_____

_____

_____

_____

_____

_____

_____

_____

_____

_____

_____

_____

_____

_____

_____

_____

_____

"[...] the only way a relationship will last is if you see your relationship as a place that you go to give, and not a place that you go to take."

- Anthony Robbins

What are you depositing
into your relationship bank account every day?
What are you withdrawing from it?

_____

_____

_____

_____

_____

_____

_____

_____

_____

_____

_____

_____

_____

_____

_____

_____

_____

_____

"We make all sorts of assumptions because we don't have the courage to ask questions.
- Miguel Angel Ruiz

Write about a time when you made an assumption
about your partner that turned out to be wrong.

_____

_____

_____

_____

_____

_____

_____

_____

_____

_____

_____

_____

_____

_____

_____

_____

_____

_____

_____

"The comfort zone is a beautiful place, but nothing ever grows there."

- Russel Greiner

What's something that you and your partner would love to do,
but still haven't?

"Don't ask yourself what the world needs. Ask yourself what makes you come alive, and go do that, because what the world needs is people who have come alive."

- Howard Thurman

What are some of your most important needs?
What makes you come alive?

_____

_____

_____

_____

_____

_____

_____

_____

_____

_____

_____

_____

_____

_____

_____

_____

_____

_____

_____

"If it is important to you, you will find a way. If not, you'll find an excuse."

- Ryan Blair

Are you making your relationship a priority?
Do you spend enough quality time with your partner?

_____

_____

_____

_____

_____

_____

_____

_____

_____

_____

_____

_____

_____

_____

_____

_____

_____

_____

_____

_____

_____

"When we're incomplete, we're always searching for somebody to complete us. When, after a few years or a few months of a relationship, we find that we're still unfulfilled, we blame our partners and take up with somebody more promising. This can go on and on until we admit that while a partner can add sweet dimensions to our lives, we, each of us, are responsible for our own fulfillment. Nobody else can provide it for us, and to believe otherwise is to delude ourselves dangerously and to program for eventual failure every relationship we enter."

- Anthony Robbins

Do you rely on your partner for your own happiness?
If so, how can you change that?

_____

_____

_____

_____

_____

_____

_____

_____

_____

_____

_____

_____

_____

_____

_____

_____

_____

_____

_____

_____

_____

"The best gift you could have given her was a lifetime of adventures."

- Lewis Carroll

Describe a fond memory of when you and your partner
traveled together.

_____

_____

_____

_____

_____

_____

_____

_____

_____

_____

_____

_____

_____

_____

_____

_____

_____

_____

_____

_____

Fill our own cup first and feed everyone else from the overflow. We must first nurture and fill our own cup with the sweet nectar of self-love, self- nurture and self-care."

- Diane Johnson

What self-care have you neglected?
(e.g., eating healthy, getting enough sleep, spending time on hobbies)
How does that affect your relationship?

_____

_____

_____

_____

_____

_____

_____

_____

_____

_____

_____

_____

_____

_____

_____

_____

_____

_____

_____

_____

_____

_____

*"You don't love someone because they're perfect,
you love them in spite of the fact that they're not."*

- Jodi Picoult, "My Sister's Keeper"

What do you do that your partner patiently tolerates?

_____

_____

_____

_____

_____

_____

_____

_____

_____

_____

_____

_____

_____

_____

_____

_____

_____

_____

_____

_____

_____

_____

_____

"We can;t change people; only a person can change themselves. We can use and arose the divine characteristics that are already in them."

– Darwin

How is your partner similar to your family?
How is your partner different from your family?

_____

_____

_____

_____

_____

_____

_____

_____

_____

_____

_____

_____

_____

_____

_____

_____

_____

_____

_____

_____

_____

_____

_____

"You can make more friends in two months by becoming interested in other people than you can in two years by trying to get other people interested in you."

- Dale Carnegie

What are some of your partner's favorite hobbies or activities?
How often do the two of you talk about these things?

_____

_____

_____

_____

_____

_____

_____

_____

_____

_____

_____

_____

_____

_____

_____

_____

_____

_____

_____

_____

_____

_____

"Trust is earned when actions meet words."

- Chris Butler

Do you follow through with promises to your partner? (think about the minor things as well - for example, do you show up on time?)

_____

_____

_____

_____

_____

_____

_____

_____

_____

_____

_____

_____

_____

_____

_____

_____

_____

_____

_____

_____

_____

*"Gratitude is a powerful catalyst for happiness.
It's the spark that lights a fire of joy in your soul."*

– Amy Collette

Describe a time when your partner sacrificed
something significant for you.

_____

_____

_____

_____

_____

_____

_____

_____

_____

_____

_____

_____

_____

_____

_____

_____

_____

"Well, it seems to me that the best relationships – the ones that last – are frequently the ones that are rooted in friendship."

- Gillian Anderson

What does your partner's ideal night of fun look like?

_____

_____

_____

_____

_____

_____

_____

_____

_____

_____

_____

_____

_____

_____

_____

_____

_____

_____

"Understanding is love' other name. If you don't understand, you can't love."

- Thich Nhat Hanh

Revisit a prior argument between you and your partner, take yourself out of the situation, and argue on your partner's behalf.

_____

_____

_____

_____

_____

_____

_____

_____

_____

_____

_____

_____

_____

_____

_____

_____

_____

_____

_____

_____

"The purpose of a relationship
is not to have another who
might complete you,
but to have another
with whom you might share
your completeness."

– Neale Donald Walsch

How are you growing/progressing in your personal life right now?

"Marriages [relationships] are much more likely to succeed when the couple experience a 5 to 1 ratio of positive to negative interactions.

- John M. Gottman

What would you say your positive to negative interactions ratio is at? *(Think about the little things, e.g., texts, hugs, little compliments, etc.)*
How can you further improve your ratio?

_____

_____

_____

_____

_____

_____

_____

_____

_____

_____

_____

_____

_____

_____

_____

_____

_____

_____

"None of us, including me, ever do great things. But we can all do small things, with great love, and together we can do something wonderful"

- Mother Theresa

How are you better today because you met your significant other?

_____

_____

_____

_____

_____

_____

_____

_____

_____

_____

_____

_____

_____

_____

_____

_____

_____

_____

_____

_____

_____

"*Intimacy is the capacity to be rather weird with someone – and finding that that's ok with them.*"

- Alain de Botton

Write about something funny and endearing that your significant other does.

_____

_____

_____

_____

_____

_____

_____

_____

_____

_____

_____

_____

_____

_____

_____

_____

_____

_____

_____

"If you want to go fast, go alone. If you want to go far, go together."
- African Proverb

Describe a time when you and your significant other
made a killer team.

_____
_____
_____
_____
_____
_____
_____
_____
_____
_____
_____
_____
_____
_____
_____
_____
_____
_____
_____
_____
_____
_____

"As we express our gratitude, we must never forget that the highest appreciation is not to utter words, but to live by them."

- John F. Kennedy

What is something that your partner frequently does on your behalf that
you may not notice or take time to appreciate?
Describe how that act affects you.

"A successful marriage requires falling in love many times, always with the same person"
- Mignon McLaughlin

Write out the story of when you first told your partner
that you loved them.

_____

_____

_____

_____

_____

_____

_____

_____

_____

_____

_____

_____

_____

_____

_____

_____

_____

_____

"Lets not forget it's you and me vs. problem. Not you vs. me"

- Steve Maraboli

How can you make conflict between the two of you constructive?

_____

_____

_____

_____

_____

_____

_____

_____

_____

_____

_____

_____

_____

_____

_____

_____

_____

_____

_____

_____

_____

_____

_____

"The big things are the little things. There must be constant appreciation for each other and thoughtful demonstration of gratitude. A couple must encourage and help each other grow."

- James E. Faust

Describe a time when your partner exceeded your expectations.

_____
_____
_____
_____
_____
_____
_____
_____
_____
_____
_____
_____
_____
_____
_____
_____
_____
_____
_____
_____
_____
_____
_____

*"Love is not about how much you say 'I love you',
but how much you prove that it's true."*

– Steemit

Pretend that a scientist observed you for a day.
What evidence would they have that you love your partner?

_____

_____

_____

_____

_____

_____

_____

_____

_____

_____

_____

_____

_____

_____

_____

_____

_____

_____

_____

_____

"May your daily choices be a reflection of your deepest values."

- Coleen Patrick-Goudreau

What are some values and principles that are shared between the two of you?

_____

_____

_____

_____

_____

_____

_____

_____

_____

_____

_____

_____

_____

_____

_____

_____

_____

_____

_____

_____

_____

"Value and appreciate the people who sacrifice their 'something' for you. Because maybe that 'something' was their everything."

- Unknown

List everything that your partner has invested in your relationship.

_____

_____

_____

_____

_____

_____

_____

_____

_____

_____

_____

_____

_____

_____

_____

_____

_____

_____

"The deepest craving of human nature is the need to be appreciated."

— William James

How frequently do you compliment your partner?
What is keeping you from doing this more often?

_____

_____

_____

_____

_____

_____

_____

_____

_____

_____

_____

_____

_____

_____

_____

_____

_____

_____

_____

"A great relationship doesn't happen because of the love you had in the beginning, but how well you continue building love until the end."

- Unknown

What qualities stood out to you about your partner
when you first met them?
How do they demonstrate some of those same qualities today?

_____

_____

_____

_____

_____

_____

_____

_____

_____

_____

_____

_____

_____

_____

_____

_____

_____

_____

"Alone we can do so little; together we can do so much"

- Helen Keller

Name three of your favorite achievements between
you and your partner.
How did the two of you work together to accomplish these things?

_____

_____

_____

_____

_____

_____

_____

_____

_____

_____

_____

_____

_____

_____

_____

_____

_____

_____

_____

_____

_____

" The best way to love someone is to help them reveal the best version of themselves. "
- Unknown

What are you doing to actively support your partner's goals?

_____

_____

_____

_____

_____

_____

_____

_____

_____

_____

_____

_____

_____

_____

_____

_____

_____

_____

_____

_____

"True love is born from understanding."

- Gautama Buddha

What did your partner love about their childhood?
What didn't they like about their childhood?

_____

_____

_____

_____

_____

_____

_____

_____

_____

_____

_____

_____

_____

_____

_____

_____

_____

_____

_____

_____

"In the best relationship, you know about each other's pasts and as a result, love each other even more."

- Unknown

What does your partner know about you that no one else does? Why did you choose to share that with them?

_____

_____

_____

_____

_____

_____

_____

_____

_____

_____

_____

_____

_____

_____

_____

_____

_____

_____

_____

_____

"Some think love can be measured

by the amount of butterflies

in their tummy. Others think love can be

measured in bunches of flowers,

or by using the words 'for ever.'

But love can only truly be measured

by actions. It can be a small thing,

such as peeling an orange for a person

you love because you know

they don't like doing it."

- Marian Keyes

What is one of the most meaningful acts of service your partner has done for you?

_____

_____

_____

_____

_____

_____

_____

_____

_____

_____

_____

_____

_____

_____

_____

_____

_____

_____

_____

" The single most important thing we can do for the person we love is love them as they most desire to be loved. "

- Fawn Weaver

What is one of the most romantic dates that you and your partner have been on?

_____

_____

_____

_____

_____

_____

_____

_____

_____

_____

_____

_____

_____

_____

_____

_____

_____

_____

_____

_____

"We often take for granted the very things that most deserve our gratitude."

- Cynthia Ozick

What compliments do others frequently give your partner?

_____
_____
_____
_____
_____
_____
_____
_____
_____
_____
_____
_____
_____
_____
_____
_____
_____
_____
_____
_____
_____

"Trouble is part of your life, and if you don't share it, you don't give the person who loves you enough chance to love you enough."

- Dinah Shore

Describe a time when you felt especially safe with your partner.

_____

_____

_____

_____

_____

_____

_____

_____

_____

_____

_____

_____

_____

_____

_____

_____

_____

_____

"Most people do not listen with the intent to understand, they listen with the intent to reply."

- Stephen R. Covey (The 7 Habits of Highly Effective People)

How much listening do you do in your relationship?
Do you try to "fix" your partner's problems?

_____

_____

_____

_____

_____

_____

_____

_____

_____

_____

_____

_____

_____

_____

_____

_____

_____

_____

_____

_____

_____

_____

"The greatest thing you'll ever learn is to love and be loved in return."
- Nat King Cole

Describe a time that your partner took care of you physically.

_____

_____

_____

_____

_____

_____

_____

_____

_____

_____

_____

_____

_____

_____

_____

_____

_____

_____

_____

_____

_____

_____

In all of living, have much fun and laughter. Life is to be enjoyed, not just endured."
- Gordon B. Hinkley

What is the easiest way to cheer your partner up?

_____

_____

_____

_____

_____

_____

_____

_____

_____

_____

_____

_____

_____

_____

_____

_____

_____

_____

_____

"Fidelity to your partner is love that speaks beyond a thousand words."

- Unknown

Describe an experience when your partner had your back.

_____

_____

_____

_____

_____

_____

_____

_____

_____

_____

_____

_____

_____

_____

_____

_____

_____

_____

_____

_____

_____

_____

"Never let a problem to be solved become more important than a person to be loved."

- Barbara Johnson

What is something that you took personally that your partner didn't intend? What were the consequences of holding on?

_____

_____

_____

_____

_____

_____

_____

_____

_____

_____

_____

_____

_____

_____

_____

_____

_____

_____

"I water you. You water me; we grow together"

- Brandon Nembhard

Describe an experience when your partner supported you through a difficult situation.

_____

_____

_____

_____

_____

_____

_____

_____

_____

_____

_____

_____

_____

_____

_____

_____

_____

_____

_____

_____

_____

_____

"We can improve our relationships with others by leaps and bounds if we become encouragers instead of critics."

- Joyce Meyer

Describe how your partner has been supportive of you
in one of your projects or hobbies.

_____

_____

_____

_____

_____

_____

_____

_____

_____

_____

_____

_____

_____

_____

_____

_____

_____

_____

_____

_____

_____

_____

" To get the full value of joy, you must have someone to divide it with. "

- Mark Twain

What would be your significant other's dream day? If you don't know, ask them and write their response down.

_____

_____

_____

_____

_____

_____

_____

_____

_____

_____

_____

_____

_____

_____

_____

_____

_____

_____

_____

_____

*"A strong relationship starts with two people who are
willing to sacrifice anything for each other"*

- Etka Rohra

What have you been willing to sacrifice for your partner?

_____

_____

_____

_____

_____

_____

_____

_____

_____

_____

_____

_____

_____

_____

_____

_____

_____

_____

"Your relationship with yourself sets the tone for every other relationship you have.

- Robert Holden

Do you take time for yourself? What are things you can do to "recharge," so you can bring my best to the relationship?

_____

_____

_____

_____

_____

_____

_____

_____

_____

_____

_____

_____

_____

_____

_____

_____

_____

_____

_____

_____

" The secret of a long life...laughter. The secret of a long-lasting relationship... laughing together"

- Unknown

Describe one of the times when you and your partner laughed the hardest together.

_____

_____

_____

_____

_____

_____

_____

_____

_____

_____

_____

_____

_____

_____

_____

_____

_____

_____

_____

_____

_____

_____

"Learn to appreciate what you have before time makes you appreciate what you had."
- Ziad K. Abdelnour

How would your life be different if you hadn't met your partner?

_____

_____

_____

_____

_____

_____

_____

_____

_____

_____

_____

_____

_____

_____

_____

_____

_____

"To fall in love and to commit yourself to love means you should make your loved one the one thing you cherish the most."

- Kou Yoneda

Why did you choose to commit to your significant other?

_____

_____

_____

_____

_____

_____

_____

_____

_____

_____

_____

_____

_____

_____

_____

_____

_____

_____

_____

_____

"The beginning of love is to let those we love be perfectly themselves, and not to twist them to fit our own image. Otherwise we love only the reflection of ourselves we find in them."

- Thomas Merton

What are some of your favorite characteristics that your partner possesses? Why are these your favorites?

_____

_____

_____

_____

_____

_____

_____

_____

_____

_____

_____

_____

_____

_____

_____

_____

_____

_____

_____

_____

"Love is a verb. Love – the feeling "– is the fruit of love the verb or our loving actions"

- Stephen R. Covey

Are you putting your best foot forward in the relationship?
Where are you holding back that you can contribute?
(Think time, energy, service, support, etc.)

_____
_____
_____
_____
_____
_____
_____
_____
_____
_____
_____
_____
_____
_____
_____
_____
_____
_____
_____
_____

"A great relationship is about two things. First, appreciating the similarities, and second, respecting the differences.

- Unknown

What are some things that the two of you have in common?
What are some differences between the two of you?

_____

_____

_____

_____

_____

_____

_____

_____

_____

_____

_____

_____

_____

_____

_____

_____

_____

_____

_____

"To be fully seen by somebody, then, and be loved anyhow—this is a human offering that can border on miraculous."

- Elizabeth Gilbert

What are some of your significant other's current stressors?
Is there anything you can do to help alleviate their stress?

_____

_____

_____

_____

_____

_____

_____

_____

_____

_____

_____

_____

_____

_____

_____

_____

_____

_____

"Is there anyone so wise as to learn by the experience of others?"

- Voltaire

Who do you think has the healthiest relationship that you've seen? What do you and your partner do that's similar?
What do you do that's different?

_____

_____

_____

_____

_____

_____

_____

_____

_____

_____

_____

_____

_____

_____

_____

_____

_____

_____

_____

"Love is a partnership of two unique people

who bring out the very best in each other,

and who know that even though

they are wonderful as individuals,

they are even better together."

- Barbara Cage

What makes you and your partner a power couple?

"Sometimes you will never know the value of a moment, until it becomes a memory."

- Dr. Seuss

What is the first memory you have of your significant other?

_____

_____

_____

_____

_____

_____

_____

_____

_____

_____

_____

_____

_____

_____

_____

_____

_____

_____

_____

" The way to get to the top is to get off your bottom. "

- Gabe Godines

What is a common goal that you and your partner share?
What can you do make progress on that goal?

_____
_____
_____
_____
_____
_____
_____
_____
_____
_____
_____
_____
_____
_____
_____
_____
_____
_____
_____
_____

"Never be too busy for the people you love.

Never allow pursuits or possessions

to become bigger priorities

than your relationships.

Love is what gives meaning to life."

- Dave Willis

What's something that your partner has asked you to do that you've delayed doing? Why do you think that matters to them?

"Be an encourager. The world has plenty of critics already."

- Dave Willis

What are some hidden talents that your partner has?

_____

_____

_____

_____

_____

_____

_____

_____

_____

_____

_____

_____

_____

_____

_____

_____

_____

_____

_____

_____

_____

" The greatest compliment that was ever paid me was when someone asked me what I
thought, and attended to my answer."

- Henry David Thoreau

In what ways does your partner positively influence you?
How frequently do you ask for their advice and opinions?

_____

_____

_____

_____

_____

_____

_____

_____

_____

_____

_____

_____

_____

_____

_____

_____

_____

_____

_____

_____

_____

_____

_____

_____

"The more rules you have about how people have to be, how life has to be for you to be happy – the less happy you're going to be."

- Anthony Robbins

What are some unfair expectations that you hold over your partner? How would letting go affect your relationship?

_____

_____

_____

_____

_____

_____

_____

_____

_____

_____

_____

_____

_____

_____

_____

_____

_____

_____

_____

_____

_____

_____

What new hobbies and interests have you developed with your partner?

_____

_____

_____

_____

_____

_____

_____

_____

_____

_____

_____

_____

_____

_____

_____

_____

_____

_____

"It is what we know already that often prevents us from learning."
- Claude Bernard

What have you learned from your partner?

"What you focus on grows, what you think about expands, and what you dwell upon determines your destiny"

- Robin S. Sharma

How do you talk about your partner with other people?

_____

_____

_____

_____

_____

_____

_____

_____

_____

_____

_____

_____

_____

_____

_____

_____

_____

_____

_____

_____

_____

*"Motivate and support your partner.
You are both a work in progress so grow and build together."*

- Gregorio Rafael

What job would your partner excel at? Why?

"You can fix almost anything you are willing to talk about."
- Larry Winget

Name a time where conflict helped the two of you grow.
How did that happen?

_____

_____

_____

_____

_____

_____

_____

_____

_____

_____

_____

_____

_____

_____

_____

_____

_____

_____

_____

_____

"The more things we can laugh about,
the more alive we become:
The more things we can laugh about
together, the more connected
we become."

- Frank Pittman

Describe your partner's humor. What do you like about it?

"No act of kindness no matter how small is ever wasted."

- Aesop

Do you feel that you are making your partners life easier?
If so, in what ways? If not, how can you make it so?

_____

_____

_____

_____

_____

_____

_____

_____

_____

_____

_____

_____

_____

_____

_____

_____

_____

_____

_____

_____

_____

"To find someone who will love you for no reason, and to shower that person with reasons, that is the ultimate happiness."

- Robert Brault

Describe a time that your partner nurtured you emotionally.

_____

_____

_____

_____

_____

_____

_____

_____

_____

_____

_____

_____

_____

_____

_____

_____

_____

_____

_____

_____

_____

- Dino Sam

What is something that comes to your partner easily but is difficult for you?

_____

_____

_____

_____

_____

_____

_____

_____

_____

_____

_____

_____

_____

_____

_____

_____

_____

_____

_____

"It's incredibly easy to get caught up in the thick of thin things."
- Stephen R. Covey

Are you holding a grudge over something your partner has done?
How can you let go of this?

_____

_____

_____

_____

_____

_____

_____

_____

_____

_____

_____

_____

_____

_____

_____

_____

_____

_____

_____

_____

"In our daily lives, we must see
that it is not happiness
that makes us grateful,
but the gratefulness
that makes us happy."

- Albert Clark

What is something that you and your partner do together that you might take for granted?

_____

_____

_____

_____

_____

_____

_____

_____

_____

_____

_____

_____

_____

_____

_____

_____

_____

_____

_____

"Motto for the bride and groom [or all relationships]:
We are a work in progress with a lifetime contract."

- Phyllis Koss

How have you and your partner grown since you first met?

_____
_____
_____
_____
_____
_____
_____
_____
_____
_____
_____
_____
_____
_____
_____
_____
_____
_____
_____
_____
_____
_____
_____
_____

"'love' is really spelled t-i-m-e"

- Dieter F. Uchtdorf

What is a non- physical gift you've received from your partner?
(Think time, attention, understanding, or support)

_____

_____

_____

_____

_____

_____

_____

_____

_____

_____

_____

_____

_____

_____

_____

_____

_____

_____

"I would maintain

that thanks are the highest form of

thought, and that gratitude is

happiness doubled by wonder."

- GK Chesteron

What did your partner do today without you having to ask?
Why was that meaningful?

_____

_____

_____

_____

_____

_____

_____

_____

_____

_____

_____

_____

_____

_____

_____

_____

_____

_____

_____

_____

_____

"Enjoy the little things in life...
For one day you'll look back and realize they were the big things."
- Robert Brault

If you could relive one day with your partner, what day would it be?

_____

_____

_____

_____

_____

_____

_____

_____

_____

_____

_____

_____

_____

_____

_____

_____

_____

_____

_____

_____

"Always remember people who have helped you along the way"
- Roy T. Bennett

What great qualities did your partner get from their family?

_____

_____

_____

_____

_____

_____

_____

_____

_____

_____

_____

_____

_____

_____

_____

_____

_____

_____

_____

_____

"We should all be thankful for those people who rekindle the inner spirit."

- Albert Schweitzer

What's one of the most meaningful compliments your partner has ever given you? Why does it mean so much to you?

_____

_____

_____

_____

_____

_____

_____

_____

_____

_____

_____

_____

_____

_____

_____

_____

_____

_____

_____

_____

" The most beautiful discovery true friends make is that they can grow separately without growing apart. "

- Elisabeth Foley

What, in your opinion, separates a good relationship from a bad one?
A good relationship from a great one?

"A great spouse loves you exactly the way you are. An extraordinary spouse helps you grow; inspires you to be, do and give your very best."

- Fawn Weaver

Name some feedback that your partner gave you that was beneficial.

"We tend to forget that happiness doesn't come as a result of getting something we don't have but rather of recognizing and appreciating what we do have."

- Frederick Keonig

Name a time when your partner showed patience when interacting with someone.

"When you love someone, you love the person as they are, and not as you'd like them to be."

- Leo Tolstoy

How can you bring more love into your relationship?

_____

_____

_____

_____

_____

_____

_____

_____

_____

_____

_____

_____

_____

_____

_____

_____

_____

_____

_____

_____

"Well, it seems to me that the best

relationships-the ones that last-

are frequently the ones

that are rooted in friendship."

Gillian Anderson

When do you and your partner have the most fun together?

"Loyalty is the strongest glue which makes a relationship last for a life time."

- Mario Puzo

Describe a time when you stood up for your partner.
Why did you do that?

_____

_____

_____

_____

_____

_____

_____

_____

_____

_____

_____

_____

_____

_____

_____

_____

_____

_____

_____

_____

_____

"I love her, and that's the beginning and end of everything."

- F. Scott Fitzgerald

How do you treat your partner differently than the rest of your friends/family members?

_____

_____

_____

_____

_____

_____

_____

_____

_____

_____

_____

_____

_____

_____

_____

_____

_____

_____

_____

"You were placed on this earth to create, not compete."

- Dr. Robert Anthony, Larry Winget, It's Called Work For A Reason

What are some of the goals that you have independent of your relationship
How can your partner best support these goals?

_____

_____

_____

_____

_____

_____

_____

_____

_____

_____

_____

_____

_____

_____

_____

_____

_____

_____

_____

_____

_____

"Compassion and tolerance are not a sign of weakness, but a sign of strength."

- Dalai Lama

What are some of the weaknesses that you currently struggle with? Is your partner aware? Are you willing to ask them for help?

_____

_____

_____

_____

_____

_____

_____

_____

_____

_____

_____

_____

_____

_____

_____

_____

_____

_____

_____

_____

_____

_____

_____

" *The most important thing in life is to learn how to give out love, and to let it come in.* "
- Morrie Schwartz

What was one of the most meaningful gifts your parter has ever given you?

_____
_____
_____
_____
_____
_____
_____
_____
_____
_____
_____
_____
_____
_____
_____
_____
_____
_____
_____
_____
_____
_____
_____

"A vision is not just a picture of what could be; it is an appeal to our better selves, a call to become something more."

- Rosabeth Moss Kanter

What do you want your relationship to look like in 20 years?

_____

_____

_____

_____

_____

_____

_____

_____

_____

_____

_____

_____

_____

_____

_____

_____

_____

_____

_____

"Life with you makes perfect sense. You're my best friend."

- Unknown

Why is your partner one of your best friends?

_____

_____

_____

_____

_____

_____

_____

_____

_____

_____

_____

_____

_____

_____

_____

_____

_____

_____

_____

The meaning of life is to find your gift. The purpose of your life is to give it away."

- Pablo Picaso

What are some of your greatest gifts?
How are you bringing these into your relationship?

_____

_____

_____

_____

_____

_____

_____

_____

_____

_____

_____

_____

_____

_____

_____

_____

_____

_____

Made in United States
North Haven, CT
23 November 2022

27096302R00070